Many People to

L.I.F.E.* Adventures Book One

*Love Inspires Families Everywhere: Stories about adoption, foster care, stepchildren, and all blended families

Written by **Anna Maria DiDio**

illustrated by **Tatiana Lobanova**

ALL AGES

Love At The Border Publishing, Philadelphia, PA
First print edition 2022.

Published in the United States of America.

Summary: A young girl from Colombia is adopted in the US and struggles with her feelings as she adapts to a new language, culture and family.

Cover design and illustrations by Tatiana Lobanova

Library of Congress Control Number: 2022903873

ISBN (paperback) 978-1-7377035-1-8

For more information, visit the author's website: www.amdidio.com

L.I.F.E. Adventures
Love Inspires Families Everywhere

A Letter to Parents

Many People to Love is book ONE in the series of L.I.F.E. Adventures – stories about adoption, foster care, stepchildren, and all blended families.

Adoption begins with separation and loss. When children are matched with families, there are joyous, loving and positive feelings as well as confused and negative emotions to sort out. I am happy to support you on this tumultuous yet rewarding journey. With that in mind, these are my top five reminders for adoptive families. As you read and experience the adventure with your new family, feel free to create your own list.

Notes on Separation and Loss: Top Five Reminders for Parents

1. Be honest and answer any questions even before the concept of adoption is fully understood.
2. Be prepared for questions and feelings, especially on your child's birthday.
3. Acknowledge your child's feelings. Anger is pain. Fear will prevent giving and receiving love.
4. Be patient. If you are able to understand the trauma and loss present in your child's life, you are in the best place to move forward in a positive and loving way.
5. Seek the support of professionals as well as other adoptive parents.

*Visit **amdidio.com** to find free resources for your adoption journey, including an audible excerpt from my memoir **Love at the Border, An Adoption Adventure**.*

This book is inspired by a true story and is dedicated to the women of Mexico who put their hearts on the line so that we could become a family. We are forever grateful.

My heart hurt when I said goodbye to Rosa. Of all the women who took care of me at the orphanage, Rosa was *mi favorita*. She made me empanadas, combed my hair, and helped me get ready for school.

Hola. My name is Carla and I was born in Colombia. The house where I lived since I was a baby was not my house. The toys I played with were not my toys. I shared a bedroom with five other girls...still, I was lonely.

Rosa's magical hands tamed my wild hair into ponytails. Her hugs smelled like geraniums. Her whispers of *I love you* made me feel warm to my toes.

But when I asked Rosa, "Do you love me best?" she always looked away and said, "I love all my girls equally."

I dreamed of being adopted, having a family
to call my own and what it would be like
to have a mommy who loved me best.

But Rosa was the only mommy I ever had.
Could I love someone new?

People came and went...asking questions...bringing strange smiles and hugs, but always takng my friends home with them.

No one seemed to want me until...

...they came. The man smiled and studied his Spanish dictionary. The girl gave me candy and presents. The woman's hug smelled like cinnamon. I didn't understand anything they said!

Rosa packed my shorts, pajamas,
ballet tights, and shoes.

Soon I was flying to the United States
to live with my new family.

Everything was different and strange in my new country.

I wanted to fly back to Colombia, squeeze Rosa, and eat empanadas.

My new home was quiet and I had my own room. The bed was mine and the toys were mine, but I missed Rosa and her geraniums. All I could do was cry.

My mom tried to brush my hair but I screamed, *"no me gusta!"* and then ran out of the room before she could touch me.

The next day, my mom called Rosa. I couldn't wait to talk to her. Finally! I would get the chance to tell her how much I missed her and that I wanted to come back.

But Rosa said, "No. You have the precious gift of a family who loves you. I need to take care of the other girls. Please don't call again until you are happy with your new family."

I still miss Rosa, but my mom makes sure I talk to her every Sunday.

We also write letters and send pictures to each other.

Surprise! All of the ingredients to make empanadas covered the kitchen counter. Then I heard a familiar voice, *"Hola mi amor!"*

My heart was full. I had so many people to love and so many who loved me. That night, I brought Mommy my hairbrush. *"Gracias for empanadas."*

About the Author

Anna Maria DiDio, MSW an adoptive mother, was inspired to write her memoir, *Love at the Border, An Adoption Adventure* after her own family journey. Now her L.I.F.E.* Adventures children's books feature stories about adoption, foster care, stepchildren, and all blended families. Anna Maria hopes that her books encourage open and honest exploration about what children are thinking and feeling within their own unique families. She can be found at home in Philadelphia walking everywhere, swimming laps, reading biographies, or baking chocolate chip cookies except when traveling to new and exciting places with her husband Richard.

*Love Inspires Families Everywhere

About the Illustrator

Tatiana Lobanova was born in Moscow, Russia, and discovered a love of drawing as a young girl. "Tanya" trained in art school and also theatre college. Upon graduation, she worked within the theatrical community as an artist and stage designer, constantly perfecting her technique for illustration and classical painting. Tanya currently works full-time as a freelance illustrator. Tanya loves gardening and amateur ballet and lives in The Hague, the Netherlands with her husband Andrey and two children.

Thank you for reading my book.
Don't forget to leave a review!

Every review is precious to me. I appreciate your feedback and need your input to make the next book better.

Please take a few minutes to let me know your thoughts.

Thank you!

Anna Maria DiDio

Visit **amdidio.com** *to find free resources for your adoption journey, including an audible excerpt from my memoir **Love at the Border, An Adoption Adventure**.*

Printed in Great Britain
by Amazon

34216947R00023